✔ KT-528-218

AS Geography
UNIT 1
2ND EDITION

AQA

Specification

A

Module 1: Core Concepts in Physical Geography

048606

THE HENLEY COLLEGE LIBRARY

Philip Allan Updates
Market Place
Deddington
Oxfordshire
OX15 0SE

tel: 01869 338652
fax: 01869 337590
e-mail: sales@philipallan.co.uk
www.philipallan.co.uk

© Philip Allan Updates 2001
This edition © Philip Allan Updates 2005

ISBN-13: 978-1-84489-027-9
ISBN-10: 1-84489-027-9

All rights reserved; no part of this publication may be reproduced, stored in a retrieval system, or transmitted, in any form or by any means, electronic, mechanical, photocopying, recording or otherwise without either the prior written permission of Philip Allan Updates or a licence permitting restricted copying in the United Kingdom issued by the Copyright Licensing Agency Ltd, 90 Tottenham Court Road, London W1T 4LP.

This Guide has been written specifically to support students preparing for the AQA Specification A AS Geography Unit 1 examination. The content has been neither approved nor endorsed by AQA and remains the sole responsibility of the author.

Printed by MPG Books, Bodmin

Environmental information
The paper on which this title is printed is sourced from managed, sustainable forests.

Contents

Introduction

■ ■ ■

Content Guidance

■ ■ ■

Questions and Answers

Introduction

About this guide

This guide is for students following the AQA Specification A AS Geography course. It aims to guide you through Unit 1, which examines the content of **Module 1: Core Concepts in Physical Geography**.

This guide will clarify:
- the content of the module so that you know and understand what you have to learn
- the nature of the unit test
- the geographical skills and techniques that you will need to know for the assessment
- the standards you will need to reach to achieve a particular grade
- the examination techniques you will require to improve your performance and maximise your achievement

This introduction describes the structure of AS Geography and outlines the aims of Module 1. It then provides an explanation of some of the key command words used in examination papers. There is also advice concerning geographical skills, and learning and revision techniques.

The Content Guidance section summarises the essential information of Module 1. It is designed to make you aware of the material that has to be covered and learnt. In particular, the meaning of key terms is made clear.

The Question and Answer section provides sample questions and candidate responses at C-grade level and at A-grade level. Each answer is followed by a detailed examiner's response. It is suggested that you read through the relevant topic area in the Content Guidance section before attempting a question from the Question and Answer section, and only read the specimen answers after you have tackled the question yourself.

AS Geography

The AS is a new examination. It has been established as an intermediate standard between GCSE and A-level, the standard being defined as that which candidates have reached at the end of one year of study of an A-level course. Candidates may decide to continue to study for another year to take the A-level, which will be maintained at the traditional A-level standard. The AS is therefore a free–standing qualification but is also part of A-level.

All students taking the AS Geography examination for this specification (syllabus) must study Module 1 (which is one of three compulsory modules) and take the examination at the appropriate time. It is one of the six modules that contribute to the full A-level qualification. The structure of the qualification and the unit weightings for AQA Specification A are set out below.

AS

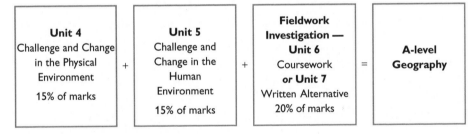

Unit 1		Unit 2		Unit 3		
Core Concepts in Physical Geography	+	Core Concepts in Human Geography	+	Geographical Skills	=	**AS Geography**
35% of AS marks *(17½% of A-level marks)*		35% of AS marks *(17½% of A-level marks)*		30% of AS marks *(15% of A-level marks)*		

A-level (AS plus the following)

Unit 4		Unit 5		**Fieldwork Investigation —** Unit 6		
Challenge and Change in the Physical Environment	+	Challenge and Change in the Human Environment	+	Coursework *or Unit 7*	=	**A-level Geography**
15% of marks		15% of marks		Written Alternative 20% of marks		

The aims of Module 1

This first module of the AS course aims to help you:
- learn and apply knowledge and understanding of physical processes
- understand the effects people have on these processes and the effects the processes have on people
- apply this knowledge and understanding at at least two scales
- develop an understanding of the relationships between people and their environments
- learn and apply geographical skills
- understand that geography is dynamic
- reflect the importance of people's values and attitudes to issues and questions

Understanding these aims will be even more important to those of you who wish to continue on to A-level. A-level includes the requirement for candidates to be aware of 'synopticity'. This means that you must be able to apply your knowledge and understanding to demonstrate the links between the different parts of the geography specification. So the modules you study at AS are relevant to your A-level answers and should not be forgotten or discarded!

Examination skills

Before looking at typical examination questions and responses in the Question and Answer section, we will examine the broader skills that are essential for success in the examination. These fall into two areas: understanding the command words; and making the most effective use of the examination paper.

The importance of command words

Command words are used by the examiners to tell you what to do in order to answer examination questions effectively. The words are set out below, in an approximate order of difficulty and skill level, with an explanation of what they mean.

Command word(s)	Meaning
Describe...	State simply what is requested. Explanation or further comment is not required.
Name/State...	Identify briefly. One word may be adequate, but it may be better to use a sentence if in any doubt.
Distinguish between...	Define and state the differences between. Linking terms, such as 'whereas' or 'on the other hand', are essential.
Outline...	Describe, with a specific focus, the geographical element requested. For example, 'Outline the main features of ...' has more of a focus than 'Describe the main features of ...'
Outline the reasons for...	Give reasons for, with a specific focus, the geographical element required. The response will be briefer than a full explanation.
Account for/ Explain/Why...?	Give reasons for. The marks will be awarded for these reasons, rather than for description.
Give reason(s) for...	Some explanation must be offered.
Describe and explain...	Both elements, description and explanation, must be present for full marks. Ensure that examples of the mentioned theme are used in the response.
Compare...	What are the similarities between? Some element of contrast may be present.
Contrast...	What are the differences between? Two separate accounts will not meet the needs of this command; there must be a specific contrast or distinction between the elements.
Examine...	Give an overview of the elements which affect the theme, i.e. outline *and* explain.
Assess/to what extent...?	This requires an assessment of the importance of the factors involved in the response. This would be in an extended prose answer, rather than a short one.

The unit test

Module 1 is assessed by Unit 1. You have 1 hour to answer this paper, which accounts for 35% of the AS Geography qualification.

There are three stimulus–response questions, one from each of the three elements: (1) Water on the land, (2) Climatic hazards and change, and (3) Energy and life. You have to answer all the questions.

Each question is marked out of 20, so there are 60 marks for the whole paper. You are advised to spend 20 minutes on each question. The spacing on the questions allows two lines per mark for your response, which is written in the question book. It is therefore useful to allocate your time accordingly. The highest number of marks (10) is for the last part, so you should allow half the time on each question for this — about 10 minutes. This part requires a longer response in more continuous prose. The examiners are looking for good organisation in these answers, especially in the final part. Remember to check the command words so that you present the appropriate responses. Try to keep within the lines allocated, but if this proves to be impossible, use the lined pages at the end of the question booklet, making sure that you have clearly indicated what you have done and have identified each response.

Response levels

The first part of each stimulus–response question is given 1 or 2 marks for each point, while the final two parts are marked according to Levels. There are criteria for reaching these Levels depending on the quality of the geographical content and the use of geographical and English language. These parts require a fuller development of geographical understanding and language skills.

Part (b) of each question is marked in two Levels; part (c) in three Levels. These are as follows:
- Level 1 (basic) responses offer one or two points without examples.
- Level 2 (clear) responses show some understanding, better use of language and make points with examples.
- Level 3 (detailed) responses show detailed understanding, make several points with examples, and use language effectively.

The command words are important, so make sure you remember to follow the instructions.

Geographical skills

As an integral part of your studies for this unit, you are required to develop a variety of skills. There are six types of geographical skill specified at AS:
- basic skills
- graphical skills
- cartographic skills

- ICT (information and communication technology) skills
- statistical skills
- investigative skills

Basic skills

Base maps
The drawing or use of photocopied base maps of a drainage basin, climatic distribution or vegetation distribution, and the use of overlays for comparison of different river basins. Annotation is an effective addition to such maps.

Sketch maps
These require you to select only relevant information to produce, for example, sketch maps of the location of hydrograph sites, management strategies in a river basin, or an urban heat island.

Atlas
The use of an atlas is essential so that global distribution of climates, biomes and soils can be identified. The atlas can also provide the basis for sketch maps.

Photographs
These are effective as an aid to interpretation, for example photographs taken of river features in the field. Other uses include the impact of climatic hazards and the characteristics of biomes.

Literacy
You need to develop literacy skills during the AS course. The assessment units require the ability to respond to both short-answer and extended prose questions.

Graphical skills

You should be familiar with the majority of these skills, but some will be new to you. You are expected to be able to interpret and construct the following.

Line graphs
Four types are specified:
- **simple line graphs**, for example hydrographs
- **comparative line graphs** — two line graphs on the same axes for comparison, for example storm hydrographs showing flashy and non-flashy rivers (you need to be aware of the use of log–log or log–normal graph paper for these graphs)
- **compound line graphs** — line graphs with amounts totalled, for example a hydrograph with the contribution of the component flows (base flow, storm flow) shown
- **divergent line graphs** — line graphs showing variation from a mean or other fixed point, which is the central horizontal axis, for example variations from the mean discharge or global temperature over a period of time

Bar graphs
Four types are specified:

- **simple bar graphs**, for example net production in biomes
- **comparative bar graphs** — bars side by side for comparison, for example to compare deforestation over time between different rainforest areas
- **compound (or divided) bar graphs** — bars divided into their components, for example the amount of discharge each tributary river contributes to the main river
- **divergent bar graphs** — bar graphs showing variation from a mean or other fixed point which is the central horizontal axis, for example variations from the mean precipitation over a period of time

Scattergraphs — and the use of the best fit line

These plot the relationship between the point data for two variables, for example flood peak discharge against time for recurrence intervals.

The best fit line is the average straight line passing between the points — the closer the points to the line, the closer the relationship between the variables. The steeper the gradient, the more rapid the change in the relationship.

There are three relationships of which you should be aware:

- **positive** — the two variables increase or decrease together and the trend of the line rises to the right, for example hydraulic radius and distance from the source of the river
- **negative** — one variable increases while the other decreases and the trend of the line falls to the right, for example discharge increasing and bedload size decreasing with distance downstream
- **no relationship** — there is no discernible trend to the pattern (this can indicate clustered data instead)

You need to be aware of the use of log–log and log–normal graph paper for scatter-graphs.

Pie charts

Pie charts use sectors of a circle to show proportions of a whole, for example the proportions of bedload particles of differing geology at a site.

Triangular graphs

These are used to show the proportions of three contributing elements, such as sand, silt and clay in a soil sample.

Lorenz curves

These show inequalities in distributions. An even distribution is shown by a straight line at 45°; the further the actual distribution is from this line, the more varied it is. Lorenz curves are not frequently used for rivers, but it would be possible to construct one to show the proportion of river flow in each continent and draw out the variation between deserts and wetter areas.

Storm hydrographs

These shows the precipitation pattern and the discharge of a river over time in response to a storm event and are covered under line graphs above.

Kite and vector diagrams

These are specialist graphs to show distribution along a transect (kite) or in a direction (vector). The former are used to show, for example, the distribution of vegetation species along a belt transect on dunes. The latter might show the orientation of prevailing winds, which influence urban climates.

Pyramids

These are used to show amounts by groups. The amount of energy found at each trophic level in an ecosystem is shown by a pyramid.

Logarithmic scales

You need to have an understanding of logarithmic scales. These are used to plot rates of change.

Cartographic skills

Ordnance Survey maps

You need to be familiar with these at a number of scales: 1:50 000, 1:25 000, 1:10 000 and 1:1250. You will be familiar with the smaller-scale maps from your GCSE studies, but the larger-scale maps/plans are of great value for work involving river studies. If these maps are not available in your centre, they are held in the reference sections of larger public libraries and in the planning departments of local authorities.

Weather maps (including synoptic charts)

You need to be familiar with weather maps that show the meteorological features covered in the specification. You must be able to recognise the standard symbols used on these maps and charts.

Soil maps

These are more specialised maps, published by the Soil Survey of Great Britain. They are usually very detailed, but you should be able to identify major podzol and brown earth soil associations. Again, these maps are often held in the reference sections of larger public libraries.

Choropleth (shading) and isoline maps

These two types of map are available for interpretation and also can be constructed from your own data.

Choropleth maps use shading to show the spatial distribution of a factor, dividing data into ranges of values represented by a different colour or texture of shading.

Isoline maps join points of equal value. Precipitation patterns (isohyets) and the velocity of water in a river channel (isovels) are two uses of these skills. Other examples include isoline maps of the distribution of soil pH values in a sample area and maps of temperature in an urban heat island (isotherms). Isoline maps show spatial changes in patterns of data.

Remember that choropleth maps should only be produced for data in the form of ratios or density and not simple numbers, whereas isolines can be used for both types of data.

ICT (information and communication technology) skills

Photographs

You need to be familiar with ground and oblique aerial photographs and be able to interpret the geographical features they depict through written answers and sketching. River channel landforms, vegetation characteristics and the effects of climatic change can be identified using photographs.

Satellite images

Land use in river basins can be identified from satellite images and used to assess land-use influences on river flooding. Areas of deforestation can also be identified.

Databases

River flow data have already been mentioned as having many uses. Climatic change data are also accessible.

Internet

This is an expanding source of information for geographers, offering an array of databases, case studies and news sources. You will not be specifically examined on this skill, though reference could be made to it. Information is available, for example, on major environmental events, river flow data and river management schemes.

Video and television programmes

You not be specifically examined on this skill, though reference could be made to these media. Major floods and other environmental catastrophes are covered.

Statistical skills

Measures of central tendency

The **mean** is the *average* value of a set of data (arithmetic mean).

The **mode** is the *most frequently occurring* value in the data set.

The **median** is the *middle value* of the data set.

Means of dispersion

You will need to know how to plot and interpret a **dispersion diagram**. This shows the range of data covered and permits a fuller understanding of the interquartile range and standard deviation.

The **interquartile range** is the range between the 25th and 75th percentage points in the data set. For example, if the data listed flood events over the last 100 years, then the interquartile range would encompass the 25th highest to the 75th highest level, i.e. 25 points either side of the median. It shows the dispersion of the data from the median and thus shows the variability of flood events for a certain discharge level.

The **standard deviation (SD)** is a statistical means of assessing the average amount by which the distribution of data varies from the mean. For example, taking the situation mentioned above, the mean flood level might be 200 centimetres. An SD of

5 cm would indicate that flood levels tend to have little variation from year to year, whereas an SD of 15 cm would indicate a wider variation, as illustrated by the following table:

Mean = 200 cm	SD = 5 cm	SD = 15 cm
Within plus or minus 1 SD (68% of values)	Between 205 and 195 cm	Between 215 and 185 cm
Within plus or minus 2 SD (95% of values)	Between 210 and 190 cm	Between 230 and 170 cm
Within plus or minus 3 SD (99% of values)	Between 215 and 185 cm	Between 245 and 155 cm

In terms of the examination, you might be expected to be aware of the skill, what the results mean and to be able to carry out some simple stages of the calculations.

Correlation tests

Spearman's rank correlation coefficient is the only correlation test you need to know. This is a relatively straightforward test to establish whether a relationship exists between two sets of ranked data and what type of relationship that might be. It is used for data shown on a scattergraph (see pp. 9–10), i.e. with positive or negative relationships. The range of results is always within the range of +1.0 (perfect positive correlation) to –1.0 (perfect negative correlation). It follows that a result closer to 0 indicates a very weak relationship (more like a clustered distribution). The minimum number of pairs of data is 6 (according to statisticians), though most geographers would expect a minimum of 10 pairs to ensure a greater reliability of the result.

This test is very frequently used in river work. The relationships between velocity, discharge, bedload etc., and in terms of distance downstream, are invariably calculated by this method. The relationship between position on a slope and soil pH, moisture etc., or temperatures from the urban core are also testable by applying this skill.

In terms of the examination, you might be expected to be aware of the skill, what the results mean and to be able to carry out some simple stages of the calculations. You will not be expected to use significance at AS.

Investigative skills

The identification of geographical questions and issues

Unit 1 provides a wide range of opportunities for investigative study. Hypotheses for testing the characteristics of rivers against theory are frequently used. Examples of some simple hypotheses include 'Bedload decreases in size downstream', 'Soil pH varies with vegetation type' and 'The urban heat island is stronger under anticyclonic conditions'.

The selection of relevant primary and secondary data and an assessment of their validity

The popularity of river fieldwork means that appropriate data can be collected. The nature of the hypotheses to be tested will define the actual data collected, e.g. velocity, cross-section, wetted perimeter, bedload, discharge, gradient, infiltration rates and so on. Secondary data on river flow are available from a number of sources, including water authorities and the Environment Agency. The Internet is a valuable means of accessing such data.

You also need to understand the reliability of the methods of data collection employed and of the data collected.

The processing, presentation, analysis and interpretation of the evidence collected

These skills are developed as the course progresses and are not confined to data collected in the field. They can be assessed in a general sense in questions in Units 1 and 2 and will not be formally assessed in Unit 3. Writing up fieldwork and analysis of data downloaded from the Internet will develop such skills. In terms of rivers, soils, vegetation or climate, a comparison of the results, interpreted in relation to theory, will fulfil the requirements of this section.

The ability to draw conclusions and show an awareness of their validity

This skill is again not confined to data collected in the field. These skills could be assessed in the general sense when responding to questions in Units 1 and 2, and will not be formally assessed in Unit 3. A conclusion to and an evaluation of the success of any geographical fieldwork exercise would be appropriate here.

The awareness of risks when undertaking fieldwork

This is essential. It is not advisable to undertake fieldwork involving rivers on your own, for example. Assistance from others is needed to collect the data and to ensure your safety in any geographical fieldwork situation.

Investigative skills are best developed by a programme of fieldwork undertaken in the AS year. Preparation for work in the field, the collection of data and their interpretation and evaluation are demonstrated clearly by writing up the fieldwork in the format suggested by the board. Your teachers will be able to advise you about this.

Techniques for learning and revision

Most of you will be taking the AS examination at the end of, or during, a one-year course, with the examination taken in January or June. This means that there is no surplus time available for teaching the subject content. You must ensure that, from the start of the course, you establish good working practices to make the most of the time available.

- It is important that you do not fall behind with work during the year. New material will be taught each week so, if you are unavoidably absent (because of illness, for example), do make sure you are able to make up the missed work as quickly as possible.
- You will probably have a steady stream of homework during the course. This is likely to take a variety of forms, ranging from working from your textbook or other sources, to practising examination questions.
- Read widely from a variety of sources, including your textbook, newspapers and magazines such as *Geography Review*. Television programmes are also relevant. The information you gather will enable you to develop a number of case studies for use in your examination answers.

If you keep on top of the work, your revision programme will be more relevant and straightforward in the lead-up to exams.

The specification is divided up into modules, as we have already seen. Each module is divided into three elements and each of these into three or four sub-elements.

Module 1: Core Concepts in Physical Geography is divided as follows:

Elements	Sub-elements
Water on the land	Drainage basin systems Channel processes and landforms Flooding and its management
Climatic hazards and change	Costs and benefits of weather and climate Climatic hazards Climatic change: the micro-scale Climatic change at global scale
Energy and life	Systems, flows and cycles The time factor Soils and the impact of human activity

Revision can be more easily structured by taking the sub-elements and focusing on them. Note that it is better to revise the sub-elements in the order in which they appear, or there might be the risk that points will not make sense!

Some tips on revision

- Having selected a topic for revision, read and learn the material you have for this topic, e.g. notes, handouts, worksheets etc.
- Refer to your textbooks and to this publication. You might also find Raw, M. (2000) *AS/A-level Geography Exam Revision Notes* (Philip Allan Updates) a useful guide.
- Learn the relevant case studies. For AS you probably need no more than two for each element/sub-element and these should be at different scales to meet the examination requirements.

- Practise sample questions, keeping to the appropriate timings. Use the questions in the last section of this guide for this purpose, taking care not to look at the sample answers and examiner's comments until you have attempted the questions. There are other specimen questions available, so consult your teacher/ lecturer for advice.
- Apply your knowledge and understanding when practising so that your answers reflect the demands of the question.
- Allow yourself adequate time for revision. Little and often is usually better than concentrated pressure at the last minute.

Content Guidance

There are three elements in the specification content for Module 1:

(1) Water on the land

(2) Climatic hazards and change

(3) Energy and life

In this section, the key concepts of each of these topics are explained, together with a breakdown of what you need to know and learn.

Details of case studies are indicated under the sub-elements. One case study per sub-element is required and the scales are indicated by the following letters:

(S) Small scale (could be fieldwork)
(R) Regional scale (smaller scale than national)
(N) National scale
(G) Global scale

Points to note
- The same cases can be used for more than one sub-element, as appropriate.
- In a small number of cases, more than one case study is specified. This is indicated at the appropriate point using the code letters above. The most frequent will be comparisons of LEDW and MEDW examples.

THE HENLEY COLLEGE LIBRARY

Water on the land

Drainage basin systems (S or R)

The river system and atmospheric processes

Systems are either closed or open. A closed system involves input, transfer and output of energy but not of matter, whereas an open system involves inputs and outputs of energy or matter into and from the system.

Rivers are open systems, with inputs and outputs of energy (solar radiation, evapotranspiration) and matter (precipitation, runoff). Energy and matter are stored within the system and transferred between the stores.

This key concept involves a basic understanding of the atmospheric processes that have an influence on the river system.

Types and intensity of precipitation (frontal, orographic and convectional)
A short heavy shower leads to faster movement of water through the system, but affects only a small area; persistent precipitation will take a longer time to have an effect over the whole basin. Snow will have a delayed effect until melting occurs.

Seasonal variations in precipitation
These will influence the river regime, with wet and dry seasons having distinctive effects on the system.

You need to:
- know what a system is and how this is applied to a river
- understand the atmospheric processes that influence the system

The hydrological cycle applied to a drainage basin

A drainage basin is the area of land drained by a river. It is surrounded by higher land, the watershed. Within each drainage basin, the river system can be described by the hydrological cycle.

The hydrological cycle: definitions
- **Precipitation** — water and ice that fall from clouds into the drainage basin.
- **Interception store** — precipitation that is trapped or stored temporarily on vegetation.
- **Throughfall** — precipitation that drips from vegetation to the ground.
- **Stemflow** — precipitation that flows down plant stems to the ground.
- **Surface store** — precipitation lying on the ground.
- **Evaporation** — the change of water from liquid to gas, returning water to the atmosphere.
- **Overland flow** — the movement of water over the ground surface to a river.

- **Transpiration** — the evaporation of moisture from the stomata of plants.
- **Infiltration** — the process by which water enters the soil.
- **Soil water store** — water stored in the soil.
- **Vegetation store** — water stored in vegetation.
- **Throughflow** — water that flows through the soil to a river.
- **Percolation** — the process by which water drains to the water table.
- **Groundwater store** — water stored in the pores and crevices of rocks.
- **Groundwater flow** — water flowing in groundwater to a river.
- **Channel store** — water stored in rivers.
- **Channel flow** — water flowing in a river.
- **River runoff** — the total discharge from the river basin.

Any changes to the inputs will have an effect on the other components of the system and any changes to the components will lead to changes to others. For example, clearance of vegetation will lead to a reduction in interception, throughfall, stemflow and transpiration; an increase in surface storage and overland flow; a decrease in infiltration, soil storage, throughflow, percolation, groundwater storage and groundwater flow. Channel storage and channel flow will increase initially as water will reach the river more quickly than previously, but river runoff will remain essentially the same overall.

The hydrological cycle in the drainage basin

Tip Complete a blank version of the diagram, putting the components in the correct positions to see how well you understand the system.

You need to:
- be able to define a river basin and how it is identified on a map
- know the names of the components of a river system, including inputs, outputs, flows/transfers and stores
- be able to define these terms
- be able to label and interpret diagrams of the hydrological cycle
- know how changes to the inputs will affect the other components of the hydrological cycle

Flood (storm) hydrographs

A hydrograph is the discharge of a river plotted on a graph. **Flood (storm) hydrographs** record the response of a drainage basin to an individual precipitation event (or storm) over a short timescale.

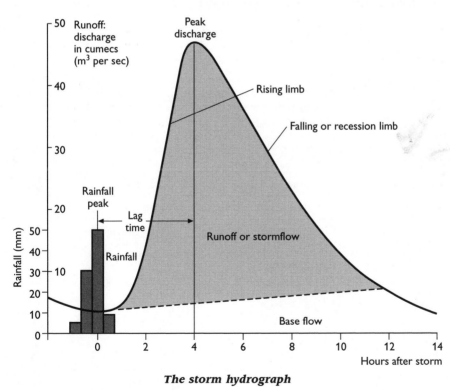

The storm hydrograph

The storm hydrograph: definitions
- **Base flow** — water that reaches the stream via groundwater flow.
- **Runoff/stormflow** — water that reaches the stream via overland flow and throughflow.

- **Peak discharge** — the time of maximum discharge after the precipitation event.
- **Rainfall peak** — the time of maximum precipitation in the precipitation event.
- **Lag time (basin lag time)** — the time between rainfall peak and peak flow.
- **Rising limb** — the increase in discharge after the start of the precipitation event.
- **Falling (recession) limb** — the decline in discharge after peak flow.
- **Discharge** — the volume of water passing a point on the river. It is calculated by multiplying the cross–sectional area (A) by velocity (V), i.e. $Q = V \times A$, and is measured in cubic metres per second (cumecs).
- **Flashy hydrograph** — one with a short lag time, with a steep rising limb and gentler, but steeper than normal, recession limb.

You need to:
- be able to define and recognise flood hydrographs
- be able to define and recognise the elements of a storm hydrograph

Discharge and the drainage basin

The response of the drainage basin to a precipitation event will vary according to the relative importance of a number of factors. These factors tend to produce either a flashy hydrograph or one with a long lag time.

Factor	Shorter lag time (flashy) — higher peak and steeper rising and recession limbs	Longer lag time — lower peak and more gentle rising and recession limbs
Basin size	Smaller	Larger
Basin shape	Circular	Elongated
Relief	Steeper slopes	More gentle slopes
Type of precipitation	Intense rainfall Rapid snow melt	Prolonged rainfall Slow snow melt
Vegetation	Absent Deciduous forest in winter	Dense Deciduous forest in summer
Land use	Deforestation Farming land Desertification	Reforestation Natural vegetation Sustainable agriculture
Urbanisation	High density	Low density
Geology	Impermeable	Permeable
Soils	Clays	Sands
Drainage density	High	Low

These factors interact to produce the discharge for the individual river basin.

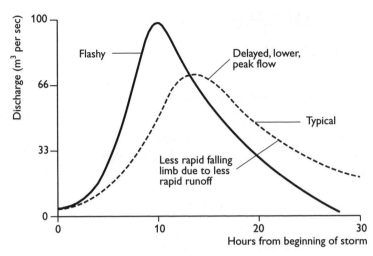

Flashy and typical hydrographs

You need to:

- identify and explain the factors that affect the shape of a hydrograph
- understand the effects of the factors that influence river discharge
- know that these factors interact with each other to produce the hydrograph shape
- understand the effects of changes to and within the hydrological cycle and their effect on the hydrograph
- apply your knowledge to one case study

The hydrograph and river flooding

The hydrograph is a summary of discharge after precipitation. Discharge will increase until the bankfull stage is exceeded. Flooding (an extreme event) is a natural process and occurs on all rivers. The conditions depend on the rate at which water reaches the river and the factors influencing the flow of water through the river system.

The frequency of a flood of a specific level is important. This is known as the recurrence (return) interval. It is found by plotting discharge against frequency and drawing the best-fit line. It can also be calculated statistically. For flood prevention, it is essential to calculate the recurrence interval for a certain level, so that, say, 50- or 100-year floods can be predicted. This will enable cost–benefit analysis to take place, as it is more cost-effective to plan flood control for a flood level that occurs frequently than for an extreme level which occurs every 100 years.

You need to:

- be aware of the links between the storm hydrograph and flooding
- be aware of the effect of extreme events on the river basin and its processes
- understand the concept of the recurrence interval and the consequences of this knowledge for people

Channel processes and landforms (S or R)

Erosion, transport and deposition

Erosion: definitions

- **Abrasion (corrasion)** — the erosion of banks and river bed by bedload.
- **Corrosion (solution)** — the solution of bed and bank material.
- **Attrition** — erosion of the bedload by contact with other load, the bed and the banks.
- **Hydraulic action** — the action of the weight of water compressing air into cracks.

The rate of erosion is related to the discharge. The greatest amount of river energy and work carried out is under bankfull conditions.

All the above processes increase with discharge. The size of river load decreases towards the mouth of the river as a result of attrition.

Transport: definitions

- **Suspended load** — load carried by the river in suspension.
- **Solution load** — load carried by the river in solution.
- **Saltation** — the movement of bedload by uplift and subsequent bouncing along the bed of the river.
- **Traction load** — the movement of bedload by rolling along the bed of the river.
- **Competence** — the largest particle that can be transported by a river.
- **Capacity** — the total load transported by a river.

Both competence and capacity increase as discharge increases.

The relationship between river velocity and capacity is not straightforward. Sand is transported at lower velocities than clay or pebbles as it is easy for the river to pick up sand particles; clay particles are more cohesive and pebbles are too large. The velocity required to keep particles in suspension is less than that needed to pick them up, so particles, once in motion, can remain aloft. Deposition of particles will occur with a small decrease in velocity.

Deposition

This occurs when the river has reduced energy; usually when velocity decreases. Reasons for deposition include:

- reduced precipitation and hence reduced discharge
- the river entering a lake or the sea
- a sudden increase in load
- shallower water in the river channel, either as a result of variations in the cross-section, or of discharge flooding out of the channel onto the floodplain

You need to:
- define and understand the four processes of erosion
- define and understand the processes of transportation
- define and understand the process of deposition
- understand the conditions under which these processes occur
- be aware of the factors that influence the relative importance of the processes within the channel, both in cross-section and downstream
- know the ways in which the variations in velocity and discharge affect the river's ability to erode, transport and deposit

The long profile of a river shows the changes in gradient from the source to the mouth. In its ideal form it is a smooth curve, decreasing in gradient. Resistant rock (waterfalls and rapids) and a fall in sea level (knickpoints) cause the most common variations from the ideal.

Channel cross-sections vary downstream too, tending to be narrower and shallower upstream and wider and deeper downstream, as discharge increases. The most efficient channels with the most energy, which enable a river to do the most work, tend to be broad and deep. Broad, shallow channels are less efficient, as demonstrated by deposition of load in braided channels.

Load

The load of a river comes from weathering on the valley slopes and the movement of this material to the river channel. It is also the result of erosion of the bed/banks of the channel. It consists of particles of varying sizes, from clay to silt, sand, gravel, pebbles, cobbles and boulders.

The type of load and where it is found will vary according to the velocity in the channel cross-profiles and long-profiles. Variations will influence channel landforms.

You need to:
- know the sources of river load
- understand where the varying types of river load are found in river channels

Landforms of river erosion and deposition

Landforms of river erosion: definitions
- **Potholes** — a rounded hole abraded by load into the resistant rock river bed.
- **Waterfall/rapids** — a sharp fall in the long profile of a river, the result of a band of resistant rock or a knickpoint. Rapids show a gentler gradient change.

Landforms of river erosion/deposition: definitions
- **Meander** — a sinuous section of the plan of a river. The shape changes as a result of erosion on the outside of the meander bend causing the meander to migrate. Deposition occurs on the inside of the bend.

- **Oxbow lake** — the result of erosion on the outside of a very sinuous meander. The meander neck is cut through, under flood conditions. Sediment is deposited along the new channel and the old meander loop is cut off, with water remaining as the oxbow lake.
- **Riffle** — a shallow section of the channel which occurs where velocity is lower between meander pools.
- **Pool** — a deeper section of the channel which occurs where velocity is greater on the outside of a meander bend.
- **Braided channel** — when a river cannot carry its load, it deposits the load in the channel. The water then cuts smaller channels in the deposited load. Thus there are several channels reworking the load in this section of the stream, with bars and islands between the channels.

Landforms of river deposition: definitions
- **Floodplain** — the area into which the river floods when bankfull stage is exceeded. The change in the river's channel cross-section causes lower competence, depositing the load. A thin layer of silt builds up with each flood.
- **Levée** — the build-up of coarser sediment at the banks of the river as it overflows its channel onto the floodplain, causing a small natural embankment. Levées are often artificially enhanced as flood-prevention measures.
- **Delta** — the result of the decrease in velocity when a river enters a lake or the sea. The coarsest sediment is deposited first and the finest last of all.

Flooding has a great effect on the formation of, and changes to, channel landforms. You need to study one river to understand the range of these landforms and how they change over time. The Mississippi is well documented, but you can study any river, possibly by personal fieldwork.

You need to:
- define and explain the main landforms associated with erosion: potholes, waterfalls/rapids, meanders and oxbow lakes
- define and explain the main landforms associated with deposition: levées, floodplains and deltas
- know how these landforms are formed and how they change with variations in discharge
- be aware of the effects of extreme events on the development of landforms
- apply this knowledge to case studies

Flooding and its management (R or N)
Definition of a hazard

A hazard is detrimental to people or property. It can have natural and/or human causes. Flooding is a natural event, but it is clear that there are human actions that contribute to floods. The hazard of flooding is increasing; there are more people living in areas liable to flood and there is greater human impact on the drainage basin.

Natural (physical) and human causes of flooding

Natural causes	Human causes
Intense precipitation events	Deforestation — more overland flow
Higher than average precipitation over a period of time	Urbanisation — shorter lag time as there is less infiltration
Already saturated ground when more precipitation falls	Development on floodplains
Rapid snow melt	Rapid snow melt (global warming)
Sea level rise	Sea level rise (global warming)
Storm surges (in coastal areas)	Drainage of wetlands

Flooding is caused by an increase in overland flow and a decrease in interception, infiltration, throughflow and groundwater flow. The hydrographs show a shorter lag time, the water exceeds the capacity of the channel and flooding occurs.

Urban areas produce shorter lag times, so development on floodplains increases the flood hazard. As more people live on floodplains, for example Maidenhead on the Thames and Dhaka in Bangladesh, the perception of the hazard is increasing as flooding occurs more frequently. The recurrence interval is shortening because of changes to land use. The influence of climatic change on sea levels is most important in coastal areas, such as southeast England and The Maldives.

You need to:
- know the physical causes of flooding
- understand the effects of intense precipitation events and the factors that affect the movement of water though the hydrological cycle and the drainage basin
- be aware of the ways in which human activity has increased the risk of flooding
- understand the effects of changes in land use, new settlement and climatic change

Examples of flooding as a hazard

This requires the study of cases from both the UK and from an LEDW area experiencing recurrent flooding (such as Bangladesh). Case studies are found in such publications as *Geography Review* (Derwent floods, 1999), and textbooks. You will find more recent examples in newspapers as they occur (October/November 2000). The causes of the individual flooding events can be identified.

River basin management in response to flooding

Many rivers have been managed in order to control any combination of the above flood causes. Flood control is one of the most important reasons for river management.

You need to:
- be aware of the reasons for river basin management in response to flooding

The strategies and responses range in scale, with contrasts evident between the LEDW and the MEDW.

It is important to cover the examples required. Two cases are needed: one from the UK and one from the LEDW. In practice, it may be preferable to use one pair of cases (e.g. LEDW — Ganges; MEDW — Severn) to cover flooding and its management.

Direct (hard engineering)	Indirect (soft engineering)
Dams	Afforestation
Barrages	Agricultural land-use management
River channel management	Urban land-use management
Flood compensation reservoirs	Urban development controls
	Flood warning systems

These strategies should be applied to your case studies in terms of which have been or which could be applied.

You need to:

- know the strategies of river management in response to flooding from your case studies
- be aware of both direct and indirect strategies from your case studies
- study a case from the UK and one from the LEDW to demonstrate the comparisons and contrasts in responses and strategies

Issues resulting from the impact of flooding and responses include:

- loss of land — displacement of people
- increase in water-borne disease
- financial costs/debt
- less effective navigation because of dams
- environmental damage
- water abstraction greater than flow downstream — river may not reach the sea
- increased erosion downstream
- sedimentation, shortening life of dam
- salinisation — higher salt content in water — affecting agriculture and fauna
- lower oxygen in water below dam affecting fauna
- political implications for international river management — may lead to conflict in certain cases

You need to:

- consider and evaluate the responses and issues arising from flooding
- know that there are variations in the effectiveness of different river management schemes in response to flooding

River management and sustainable development

Sustainable development means that the needs of the present are met, without causing problems in the future. River basin flood management schemes should not cause deterioration in the environment, economy or resource availability for future generations. Questions that need to be asked are:

- have schemes been effective to date?
- what will they be like in 50 years?
- will they be as effective in the future?
- what procedures will ensure that effectiveness is maintained, and should these be implemented?

You need to:

- be able to define sustainable development
- consider the relationships between river basin flood management and sustainable development

Climatic hazards and change

Costs and benefits of weather and climate (R or N)

The global distribution of climates

Climate is defined as the average long-term weather conditions for an area. Weather is defined as the current conditions of the atmosphere at a local scale. There is a pattern to the world distribution of climates. This is influenced by solar radiation, the distribution of land and sea, ocean currents, prevailing winds, altitude, temperature and precipitation.

You need to:

- have an understanding of the broad distribution of world climates
- know in outline the factors that have influenced this pattern

Cool temperate western maritime (CTWM) climate and its characteristics

You must study this climatic type, know where it is found and be able to locate it on a world map. You must be able to discuss the characteristics of the climate, including the temperature and precipitation patterns by season, and understand the factors that lead to these characteristics.

Characteristic	Cool temperate western maritime
Temperature	Warmer in summer, cooler in winter; smaller range
Precipitation	Occurs all year round; frontal, convectional and orographic
Winds	Westerly prevailing
Pressure systems	Lower in winter, higher in summer, but can vary greatly
Air masses	Mostly tropical maritime and polar maritime; meet at polar front
	Also experiences tropical and polar continental and arctic maritime

You need to:
- understand the environmental control and atmospheric processes which are responsible for the characteristics of this climate type
- be able to outline and understand the causal factors of this climate type

Opportunities and constraints for people

The CTWM climate provides opportunities and constraints for human activities. Agriculture, water management, tourism, flooding and drought are the main areas of interaction.

The climate affects people in different ways and the responses reflect the level of economic development in these areas.

These opportunities and constraints are dependent on seasonal and spatial variations. For example, the western maritime climate is typified by warm summers and cool winters with more precipitation in winter; mountains are an important influence on precipitation. Case studies at a regional level are essential. Northwest Europe (CTWM) is a good case study to demonstrate this climate.

You need to:
- have an understanding of the opportunities for and constraints on human activity in areas experiencing this climatic type
- be aware of variations in the climatic pattern, in both space and time
- have studied example case studies of this climatic type. These need to be at the regional scale, i.e. as areas, rather than by national boundaries
- integrate the location of the climate type, its characteristics and causal factors and the opportunities for, and constraints on, human activity

Climatic hazards (R or N)

Climatic hazards occur as short-term weather conditions. There are two main types for study here: strong wind and drought.

The definition of a hazard has been covered under flooding above.

You need to:
- be able to define a climatic hazard
- be aware of the types of climatic hazard and how these are classified

Strong wind

There are three hazards identified here: severe gales, tropical revolving storms (including hurricanes) and tornadoes. All are products of intense pressure gradients.

Severe gales are associated with deep depressions in mid-latitudes. The strongest winds occur with the passing of warm and cold fronts, although any part of the depression can experience such winds. The great storm of 1987 in southeast England is a case in point. These storms can be very destructive and cause coastal flooding.

Tropical revolving storms develop from troughs of low pressure in the easterly winds. Under certain conditions they can develop into hurricanes: 5°–20° of latitude away from the equator, with a sea surface temperature of more than 26°C in autumn (maximum sea temperature) so that (usually) large amounts of water vapour condense and release latent heat. They dissipate over land or outside the tropics. These storms have strong winds, intense precipitation, and can cause coastal storm surges, flooding and landslides; they are up to 400 km across. Hurricanes are a seasonal annual event and a recent case study is usually available.

Tornadoes occur at cold fronts in summer at the meeting of cold dry polar air and warm moist tropical air. They have a very low central pressure, very strong winds and are extremely destructive. They are very short-lived (20 minutes on average), are 100–400 metres wide and travel at 50–90 kilometres per hour. Tornado Alley in the USA provides an annual case study.

You need to:
- understand strong winds, including severe gales, tropical revolving storms (including hurricanes) and tornadoes
- locate the parts of the world in which these hazards occur
- identify the characteristics of each of these hazards
- be able to explain the causes of each of these hazards

The impact of hazards

The impact of the hazards studied in this section varies in different parts of the world. It depends on the level of economic development (MEDC or LEDC), cultural perceptions and the intensity of the hazard itself. Study of the contrasts between MEDCs and LEDCs in terms of the impact of the hazard and the responses to the hazard event is essential. Case studies at regional or national scales are required.

A number of these hazards occur every year. Tornadoes and hurricanes/cyclones are reported in the news (e.g. Hurricane Mitch) while textbooks contain older examples, such as the 1987 storm in southeast England and Hurricane Hugo. The impact of these events and the responses to them are usually reported in the media as they occur.

You need to:

- know that the impact of these hazards varies in different parts of the world
- know that responses to these hazards vary in different parts of the world
- be aware that there are different impacts and responses arising from variations in culture, the level of economic development and the intensity of the hazard event
- compare and contrast impacts and responses in the MEDW and the LEDW
- study cases of impact and response at the regional or national scale

Climatic change: the micro-scale (S)

Small-scale climatic change occurs in urban areas. The effects are more marked in larger urban areas and include modifications in temperature, humidity, precipitation, winds and air quality.

Parameter	Effects	Cause
Temperature	Higher within urban margin, increasing towards centre; best observed under anticyclonic conditions just before dawn	Solar radiation absorbed and released from buildings; central heating energy released from buildings
Humidity	Lower in urban areas	Higher urban temperatures; less transpiration from vegetation
Precipitation	Higher in large urban areas; higher downwind of urban area; less snow, frost; more fog	More convection due to heating; more particulate matter allows precipitation to develop; higher temperatures
Winds	Lower velocity, but more turbulence; increase in funnelling	Effects of rougher urban landscape due to buildings of different heights; modern buildings make narrow passageways for wind
Air quality	Lower — photochemical smog	More particulate matter; more pollution from internal combustion engines
Sunlight	Lower	More cloud; more particulate matter reflects radiation

THE RENAL SYSTEM — ACTIVITY

You need to:
- be aware of the types of change of climate that occur at a small scale in urban areas
- know and understand how and why the urban landscape can modify temperature, humidity, precipitation, winds and air quality
- know and understand the urban heat island, patterns of humidity influenced by variations in density of land use, the effects of buildings on temperature and radiation, the effects of buildings on wind speeds (including channelling) and air quality

Urban air pollution

The main type of urban air pollution is now photochemical smog (caused by exhaust gases and hydrocarbons from motor vehicles plus the effects of sunlight). The ideal weather conditions for the formation of photochemical smogs are anticyclonic, where the pollution cannot escape because of an inversion. Radiation at night causes the air in contact with the ground to be cooled, which prevents the escape of pollution because the unpolluted air above is warmer.

You need to:
- be able to define photochemical smog
- be aware of the causes of smog
- know the atmospheric processes that contribute to the formation of smog
- know the human activities responsible for the formation of smog
- have studied one case study

The effects on people

Urban air quality changes have an impact on people. Pollution causes respiratory illnesses, in particular. Lead from car exhausts also affects people. For many years, measures have been taken by governments to reduce the effects of air pollution.

Hazard	Strategies
Photochemical smog	Use of catalytic converters; strategies to reduce the use of cars — road charging, fuel taxes, public transport priority lanes, restrictions by days of the week, car sharing
Lead	No longer used in car fuel

The success of these policies should be considered.

Photochemical smog is a growing issue as the use of the car is increasing in most urban areas. Although the problems are well known and understood, there is a reluctance by motorists to give up this freedom of movement. The government currently has a number of policies under review, but has not resolved the dilemma. Any restriction on the use of the motor car involves personal values and attitudes and such issues are not easy to resolve.

You need to:

- know and understand the impact changes in air quality have had on human activity, including effects on health, the economy and society
- have studied the responses and strategies that have been employed to alleviate the effects of these changes
- use one case study
- evaluate the success of the strategies employed in the case study
- analyse the attitudes and values of decision-makers in considering this issue (e.g. what are the competing viewpoints?)

Climatic change: the global scale (G)

Global warming

Global warming is a consequence of the greenhouse effect. The greenhouse gases (water vapour, carbon dioxide, CFCs, methane and nitrogen oxides, in decreasing importance) absorb long-wave radiation from the Earth and thus prevent it from escaping into space. This raises the Earth's temperature. In recent years this natural process has been accelerated by these gases as they are all (except water vapour) increasing in the atmosphere as a result of human activity.

Greenhouse gas	Source
Water vapour	Evaporation, transpiration
Carbon dioxide	Respiration, burning of fossil fuels, deforestation and burning
CFCs (chlorofluorocarbons)	Aerosols, refrigerators
Methane	Decaying vegetation, landfill, cattle
Nitrogen oxides	Fertilisers, vehicle exhausts

You need to:

- be able to define global warming
- know the greenhouse gases, their origins and their relative importance
- be aware that some greenhouse gases are of natural origin and some are of human origin
- be able to explain why global warming is of increasing importance, although the evidence is challenged by some authorities

The effects on climate and people

The actual impact of global warming on any one area is open to some conjecture, depending on the computer model used. Some of the possible impacts on the UK and an LEDC are set out in the table below.

UK	Bangladesh (LEDC)
Warmer and wetter; seasonal rainfall stronger; more like a Mediterranean climate; alternatively, other models emphasise increased rainfall all year	Increase in storms and cyclones (hurricanes)
Coastal flooding increases as sea level rises due to expansion of water in the oceans with higher temperatures; this will cause displacement of population, industry and agriculture	Increased flooding as sea level rises due to expansion of water in the oceans with higher temperatures; this will cause displacement of population (most of the country is only a few metres above current sea levels)
Changes to crops; more maize and Mediterranean-type crops	Longer wet season; longer growing season
Water supply problems in summer	More variability in the monsoon; negative impact on agriculture
Increased disease and pests — malarial mosquitoes, brown-tailed moth (causes an itching rash)	Economic costs too great for country to respond

You need to:
- know the effects of global warming on the climate of the UK and one LEDC
- include effects on weather (warmer, wetter or drought), coastal areas as sea levels rise, agriculture and general plant growth, and on animal distribution

Political responses to global warming

There are a number of responses to this issue being undertaken by governments, though the level of response depends on a country's circumstances. The Maldive Islands, for example, are very concerned as their land is only a few metres above sea level. The USA, on the other hand, is heavily dependent on fossil fuels and does not see global warming as a serious enough issue to necessitate a cut-back on fuel consumption, though it is offering to plant forests in order to absorb carbon dioxide from the atmosphere.

There have been three major global conferences to coordinate strategies in recent years: the Earth Summit of 1992 (energy saving); the Montreal Protocol of 1986 (CFC reduction); and the Kyoto Summit of 1998 (energy reduction to reduce the use of fossil fuels). The use of CFCs has declined very rapidly and substitutes are in place. However, there has been little progress globally in the reduction of the burning of fossil fuels. The UK government has agreed to reduce the output of carbon dioxide by 50% by 2010, but the US takes a different view. Countries in the LEDW are also concerned that proposals to reduce carbon dioxide will restrict their economic growth and perpetuate the dominance of the MEDW.

The most common strategies to tackle global warming include limitations on the use of fossil fuels; the use of alternative energy sources; increased fuel efficiency; controls on deforestation; afforestation; and the international agreements mentioned above.

You need to:

- be aware of the strategies currently employed to reduce the impact of global warming
- be able to evaluate the effectiveness of such strategies
- know about the political responses to global warming including the Montreal Protocol and the Earth Summit
- be aware of and understand the values and attitudes underlying these varying political responses

Think globally, act locally

This issue brings out the concepts of sustainable development and global interdependence. These relate to the interrelationships between the LEDW and the MEDW in terms of trade, investment, aid and migration. The relationship is frequently seen as one-sided, but there can be benefits for both sides. In this case, global warming cannot be tackled without the cooperation of all countries. However, the individual can make a difference by following a sustainable lifestyle, which reduces the use of energy and greenhouse gases. Recycling, walking, cycling, using public transport etc. are all examples of individual decisions, which collectively can make a contribution.

You need to:

- be able to define sustainable development and global interdependence
- understand the relationships between the two concepts to include the potential impact of global warming on economic development in LEDCs and MEDCs
- be aware of your own values in relation to global warming — this could include your own attitudes towards consumption and recycling, public versus private transport, the use of fossil or renewable fuels etc.
- consider the concept 'think globally, act locally'

Energy and life

Systems, flows and cycles (S/G)

Ecosystems and biomes

An ecosystem is defined as a living system of plants and animals which interacts with the physical environment. On the other hand, a biome is defined as a major climax community of plants and animals which has reached equilibrium with the environment.

An ecosystem consists of biotic (living) and abiotic (non-living) components. The biotic component comprises plants and animals; the abiotic component comprises soils, air, water etc.

You need to:
- know the definitions of 'ecosystem' and 'biome' and be able to distinguish between them
- be able to define the terms 'biotic' and 'abiotic'

Energy flows through an ecosystem

Energy flows through an ecosystem from one trophic level to another. The initial source of energy is the sun. This energy is converted into plant matter by photosynthesis. At each trophic level 90% of energy is lost at transfer by respiration, excretion, decomposition and heat loss. This means that a smaller number of species can be supported at the next trophic level. The components are summarised in the table below.

Trophic level			Example	Energy %
4	Omnivores	Tertiary consumers	Fox	0.1
3	Carnivores	Secondary consumers	Weasel	1
2	Herbivores	Primary consumers	Vole	10
1	Plants	Autotrophs or producers	Grass	100
Input	Solar energy			

Decomposers (bacteria and fungi) operate at all trophic levels, as do detritivores (e.g. worms and other soil fauna) which break down dead organic material).

The movement of energy up the trophic levels demonstrates the food chain, a simple way of describing the order in which species feed on each other. A food chain is demonstrated in the 'Example' column of the table above. In reality, the relationships are more complex as some species can occupy more than one position; for example, the vole is eaten by a variety of species, which in turn can be prey for other carnivores and omnivores. This arrangement is called a 'food web'.

You need to:
- know the inputs, flows and outputs of energy
- define and explain the concept of trophic levels
- be aware of the consequences of the energy losses at each level
- be able to define and explain the roles of producers (autotrophs), consumers (herbivores, carnivores, omnivores) and detritivores
- understand food chains and food webs and the flow of energy through them
- study an ecosystem at a small-scale by fieldwork or other means

Nutrients are cycled in an ecosystem

Nutrients are essential for the production of organic material and are recycled continuously. Plants take up nutrients from the air and from the soil water. The inputs come from weathered rock and the atmosphere; the outputs are leaching from the soil and the removal of organic matter from the ecosystem. The most important nutrients are carbon, nitrogen, phosphorus and sulphur. There are many others, called trace elements, including aluminium, iron and sodium. These are taken up by plants, passed on to herbivores, carnivores and omnivores, and then detritivores reduce them to their original state by decomposition back into the soil.

The carbon cycle is illustrated in the following diagram:

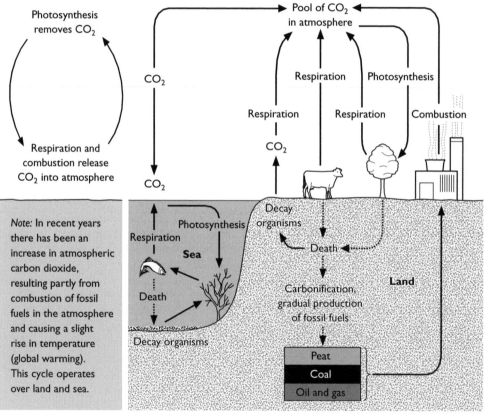

The carbon cycle

Within an ecosystem, nutrients are held in three nutrient stores: litter, biomass and soil. In tropical rainforest, the largest store is in the biomass, with the soil next and litter the smallest. In temperate grassland, the largest store is in the soil, followed by the biomass and then the litter. This reflects the temperature, rainfall and other environmental conditions influencing the ecosystems. The nutrients are transferred between the stores as part of the cycling process.

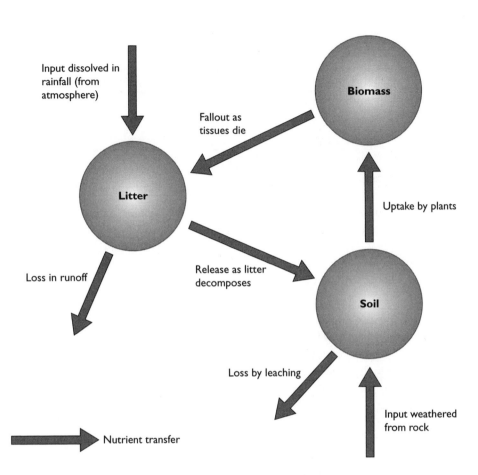

The mineral nutrient cycle

You need to:

- know the inputs, flows and outputs of nutrients
- study one example of nutrient cycling out of the carbon, nitrogen, phosphorus or sulphur cycles
- know and understand the nutrient stores and transfers between them
- study an ecosystem at a small scale — this could be done by fieldwork or other means

Productivity varies

The productivity of an ecosystem is the amount of organic material produced. It is measured in dry grammes per square metre per year. The net productivity is the primary production less respiration ($N = P - R$). Productivity varies between ecosystems because of variations in solar radiation, precipitation, latitude, temperature and length of growing season. Many natural ecosystems are more productive than agricultural ones as they maximise the use of solar energy (agricultural ecosystems have bare ground and organic matter is removed in the harvest).

You should be able to explain the productivity of the tropical rainforest ecosystem/biome in the table below in terms of the factors mentioned above.

Biome/ecosystem	Net primary productivity (g/m²/yr)
Tropical rainforest	2200
Deciduous woodland	1200
Tropical grassland	900
Coniferous forest	800
Mediterranean	700

The tropical rainforest has unique characteristics. Its location means it is the most productive ecosystem. The low latitude gives maximum insolation all year and temperatures are typically always over 27°C. Thus, there is a year-round growing season. Rainfall is over 2000 mm each year and there is generally no dry season. However, if there is one, it lasts 2 or 3 months.

These characteristics result in a distinctive ecosystem. Nutrients are cycled quickly, with most of the large biomass held in the living vegetation, not in the soil. Vegetation is well adapted to the conditions, with stratification of the plants into layers: ground, shrub, lower canopy, canopy and emergents. The specialised vegetation occupies distinct niches in the ecosystem, as does the great variety of animal life. The rainforest contains more plant (200) and animal (30) species per hectare than any other ecosystem.

You need to:
- be able to define the productivity of an ecosystem
- understand the factors that affect the productivity of an ecosystem, including latitude, insolation, water, temperature and length of growing season
- select one biome as your case study — this must be the tropical rainforest (G)

The time factor (S or R/N)

Succession and climatic climax

Time is an important factor in the development of ecosystems. A sere is a community of plants that forms a stage in the development of vegetation over a period of time. The complete sequence of seres, from the initial colonisation by pioneer communities to the climatic climax, is known as a prisere. The climatic climax vegetation is best adapted to the climatic conditions and is dominant over a large area (as in a biome). In reality, other factors, such as soils, drainage and relief, also have an impact and polyclimax is a more appropriate term. There are four priseres: lithosere (bare rock), psammosere (sand), halosere (salt water) and hydrosere (fresh water).

A typical prisere (lithosere) might consist of the following sequence of seres:

algae/bacteria – lichens/liverworts – herbs/grasses/small flowering species – ferns/bracken/small shrubs/brambles – large shrubs/small trees – large trees.

You need to:
- be able to define and understand the concepts of succession and climatic climax
- study one example of a prisere, such as a lithosere, psammosere, hydrosere or halosere

Human impact — secondary succession

People interfere with primary succession. The break in succession, if maintained, is a plagio-climax. Grazed chalk downland is a good example. However, if the break in succession is natural it is a sub-climax. Some causes are listed in the table below.

Sub-climax	Plagio-climax
Fire (lightning)	Grazing
Periodic, repeated flooding	Overgrazing
Mudflow	Deforestation
Landslide	Afforestation
Poor natural drainage (waterlogging)	Fire (deliberate)
Volcanic ash/lava flows	Agriculture

If succession restarts after a sub-climax or plagio-climax, it is secondary succession. The clearance of the rainforests over centuries has established secondary forest in much of southeast Asia. The succession that occurred after the 1883 eruption on Krakatoa is also secondary.

Relevant case studies include the effects of human intervention on deciduous woodland and of acid rain on forests in northwest Europe, as well as pollution of aquatic ecosystems in the UK.

You need to:
- define and understand the concepts of secondary succession, sub-climax and plagio-climax
- study these in terms of the human impact on deciduous woodland in northwest Europe
- study these in terms of the impact of acid rain on vegetation in northwest Europe

Deforestation

Deforestation occurs for a number of reasons, including physical, economic, social and political/cultural factors. The main example for study is the tropical rainforest. Deforestation has occurred, and is still occurring, at a rapid rate; examples include Amazonia and Indonesia. One case must be studied to allow analysis of the physical, economic, social and cultural factors which have resulted in the current situation.

If Amazonia is selected, you must consider the impact on, and interests of, the indigenous population and the new settlers. These interests are not usually compatible and are affected by the interests of those far away from the forests.

Reasons for deforestation	Consequences	Response
Subsistence agriculture	Indigenous population uses slash and burn techniques — produces secondary forest; ecosystem remains generally in balance	System in balance, but as population pressure increases, deterioration occurs
Agriculture	Forest cleared for new settlers; soil erosion, loss of biomass/nutrients, especially potassium; contribution to global warming; loss of fertility causes land to be abandoned after a few years	Government defends policy of giving land to new settlers as part of transmigration policy to ease pressure on the towns and other, poorer, rural areas (e.g. Amazonia, Indonesia)
Ranching	Forest cleared for commercial cattle ranching; same effects on soils and environment as agriculture	Transnational corporations (TNCs) blamed for causing deforestation, e.g. McDonald's; this is denied; increasing involvement of non-governmental organisations (NGOs) and environmental groups such as Greenpeace and Friends of the Earth
Logging and woodpulp	Originally, this was selective for widely scattered species, but now wholesale clearance is needed for the same result; unwanted timber is left to rot or used for MDF; same effects on soils and environment as agriculture	As above; in addition, sustainable policies increasingly applied; replanting now occurs; MEDCs will no longer accept supplies unless from sustainable sources, both by legislation and by consumer demand
Mining	Dramatic impact on landscape; causes severe soil erosion and water pollution	Little response from national governments either in country of origin or in country of receipt as metals are needed; country has valuable source of income; role of TNCs crucial here; some campaigns are developing in MEDCs (e.g. Shell Oil production in Nigeria)

You need to:

- understand the various causes of deforestation, including physical, economic, social and political/cultural factors
- study the impact of deforestation in the tropical rainforests, including physical, economic, social and cultural factors in relation to both new settlers and the indigenous population
- select one case study, such as Indonesia or Amazonia

Values and attitudes

It is clear that the number of vested interests involved in deforestation is great. The level of economic and political power that each one has also varies, both within and outside the country. Values and attitudes to deforestation also vary.

Your own attitudes and values, even at a distance from events, can have an influence. Your consumer choices have an effect on sales of timber, fast foods and species at risk of extinction. Some people become members of Greenpeace or Friends of the Earth and actively support the aims of these pressure groups.

You need to:

- analyse and understand the values and attitudes expressed by interested parties, including those of indigenous people, settlers, governments, international agencies (UN, World Bank), NGOs and pressure groups (Greenpeace, Oxfam, Friends of the Earth)
- analyse your own values and attitudes regarding this issue

Soils and the impact of human activity (S or R/N)

Factors in soil formation

Soils are the result of interaction among animal, mineral and organic components. The main factors of soil formation are parent material, climate, relief, organisms and time.

Soils are divided into horizons. An idealised soil would have the following structure:

An idealised soil profile

These horizons are distinctive in terms of their characteristics: texture, structure, acidity, organic content and water content.

Soils can be classified into three soil types, dominated by one causal factor. A zonal soil is one whose main characteristics have been determined by climate. An azonal soil is one that is permanently immature (e.g. on steep slopes). An intrazonal soil is one whose main characteristic is determined by parent material (e.g. soils on chalk).

You need to:

- be able to define and understand the origins of soil
- be able to define zonal, azonal and intrazonal soils
- understand the factors that influence soil formation

Soil properties

Soil properties may vary in each horizon and are outlined in the table below.

Soil property	Definition	Importance
Mineral matter	Particles formed as a result of weathering of the parent material	Provides the mineral component of the soil
Soil texture	The size of the particles of mineral matter in the soil — clay, silt, sand, coarse sand (loam is 40% sand, 40% silt and 20% clay)	Controls pore spacing, affecting water and air content and water flow
Organic matter	Material/particles derived from decaying vegetation/animals or faeces; breaks down into humus	Major source of nutrients; holds water; binds soil particles together
Soil structure	The joining together of the mineral and organic particles to form peds — crumb, granular, platy, blocky, prismatic, columnar	Affects water flow, air content and root penetration; influenced by vegetation
Soil moisture	The water held in the soil: gravitational (which drains away and is not available to plants); capillary (available to plant roots); and hygroscopic (unavailable to plants)	The medium by which nutrients are moved in soil (translocation); affects drainage conditions; medium of leaching (minerals in solution) and eluviation (particles in suspension)
Soil air	Fills pore spaces not filled by water; contains more CO_2 and water vapour and less O_2 than air in the atmosphere as a result of bacterial action	Essential for plant growth and respiration of organisms
Soil organisms	Living organisms found in the soil, e.g. bacteria, fungi and earthworms	Decomposition of organic matter (nutrient cycling), nitrogen fixing, development of structure

Soil property	Definition	Importance
Soil nutrients	Chemical elements found in the soil which help maintain its fertility	Essential for plant growth; can be translocated (moved) in soil water
Soil acidity	The logarithmic measure of the concentration of hydrogen ions (pH): acid < pH 7; alkaline > pH 7; and neutral — pH 7	Affects plant growth; in UK best is slightly acid; very acid or alkaline inhibits plant growth

The study of these characteristics should be undertaken by investigation of soils in a small area.

You need to:
- be able to define the main soil characteristics, including texture, structure, acidity and water content
- explain how these characteristics result in different soil horizons
- study soils in a small area to provide examples of these characteristics

Podzols and brown earths

Two of the main zonal (climatic-based) soil types found in the UK are brown earths and podzols. The main characteristics are demonstrated in a diagrammatic comparison of the soil profiles.

L	Litter layer
F	Fermentation layer
H	Humus layer
A	Acid mor
Ea	Eluvial (albic) horizon, bleached, depleted of iron and strongly acidic
Bh	Black illuvial horizon
Bfe	Iron pan (indurated horizon)
Bs	Orange-brown illuvial horizon enriched with iron Strongly acidic
C	Parent material Little altered sands and gravels or sandstone

A typical podzol soil profile

Podzols are found under boreal coniferous forest and heathland, especially on sandy, freely drained soils. They have the following characteristics.

- Low temperatures cause low evaporation, but precipitation exceeds evapotranspiration and soil water percolates downwards. Leaching removes soluble minerals and eluviation removes clay and humus particles from the upper horizons (A and E).
- Humic acids from the organic layers (L, F, H, mor) intensify the leaching process (cheluviation).
- A and E horizons consist of bleached, ash-grey sand with a high soil acidity (pH 3–5) because of the lack of clay, humus and nutrients.
- The B horizon has redeposited iron and aluminium, giving an orange-brown colour (Bs). There may be layers of humus particles (Bh) and iron pan (Bfe) where illuviation (deposition) is concentrated.
- Horizons are very clearly defined, because of the processes described above. In addition, the high acidity limits soil fauna and there is no mixing of horizons.

Typical brown earth soil profile

Brown earths are found under temperate deciduous woodland, commonly on clay soils. They are characterised by the following.

- There is a small surplus of precipitation over evapotranspiration, resulting in slight leaching. Soils are consequently mildly acidic (pH 6–6.5). The humus is nutrient-rich (mull) and there are many soil fauna.

THE HENLEY COLLEGE LIBRARY

- The clays and humus are not removed or redeposited, and the abundant fauna lead to the lack of clear soil horizons.

You need to:
- study the characteristics of two zonal soils, podzols and brown earths   (G)
- understand the conditions that favour the formation of these soils
- be able to compare and contrast the two soil types

The soil catena

This is defined as the changes in soil characteristics down a slope. Catenas develop because the topography causes changes to soil drainage characteristics according to the position and the gradient on the slope. For example, a typical soil catena in the Pennines might comprise: peaty gley podzols on flat, poorly drained summits; podzols on the free-draining slopes; and gley soils on poorly drained slope foot areas.

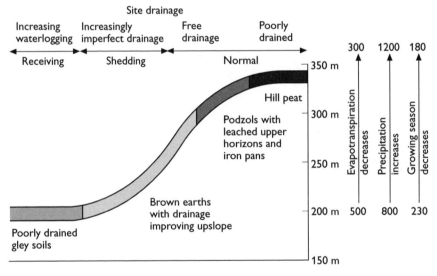

A soil catena in northern England

content guidance

Questions
&
Answers

This section of the guide contains three typical questions for Assessment Unit 1, based on the topic areas outlined in the Content Guidance section.

Sample answers are given after the questions. These are provided at a typical grade-C standard (Candidate A) and a good grade-A standard (Candidate B).

Examiner's comments

The examiner's comments are preceded by the icon e. They are interspersed in the answers and indicate where credit is due. In the weaker answers, they also point out areas for improvement, specific problems and common errors such as poor time management, lack of clarity, weak or non-existent development, irrelevance, mis-interpretation of the question and mistaken meanings of terms.

Most marks are awarded according to 'Level' attained. For each question:
- part (a) is points marked
- part (b) has two Levels:
  - Level 1 (basic) 1–3 marks
  - Level 2 (clear) 4–5 marks
- part (c) has three Levels:
  - Level 1 (basic) 1–4 marks
  - Level 2 (clear) 5–7 marks
  - Level 2 (detailed) 8–10 marks

question 1

Water on the land

(a) The diagram below shows a storm hydrograph for an area of pastureland after a rainstorm.

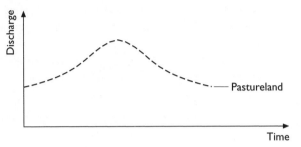

Add to the diagram the likely hydrographs following the same rainstorm in areas of similar physical conditions for:
(i) an area of dense woodland
(ii) an urbanised area (5 marks)
(b) Explain the differences in the shapes of the hydrographs shown in (b). (5 marks)
(c) Why is flooding an increasing issue in the UK? (10 marks)

■ ■ ■

Answer to question 1: Candidate A

(a)

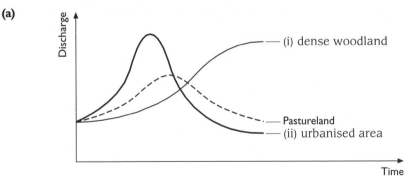

  Candidate A has identified the urban hydrograph correctly, but shows confusion over the woodland one. This is another factual question — the diagrams will be either right or wrong. The key is to identify that the pasture hydrograph will be between the urban and the woodland hydrographs. Candidate A gains 2 marks out of 5.

(b) The urban hydrograph has a steep rising limb and more gentle recession limb. The lag time is short. This is because the urban area has few trees to intercept and the land surface is tarmac. Water cannot infiltrate and runs off to the rivers quickly in

51

the drains. The woodland hydrograph has a very long lag time and this is because the trees intercept a lot of the water. More water can soak into the ground and it reaches the river slowly. The water eventually reaches the river and the discharge increases rapidly and is very great.

 The response does try to explain the hydrographs. The urban explanation is mostly correct, with some geographical language. The confusion over the woodland explanation is reflected in the inaccuracy seen in part (b), but some elements are correct. However, the use of English and geographical terminology is less secure than would be expected in a grade A response. This answer is at the top of Level 1, gaining 3 marks.

(c) Flooding is quite common in the UK. Flooding occurs for a number of reasons. Deforestation causes flooding. The removal of the trees means that there is less interception and infiltration, and overland flow occurs. As more land is used for farming, more surface runoff takes place. Urban areas now cover more of the UK and this means that the land surface does not allow water to infiltrate. The water reaches the rivers in drains more quickly. People now build on floodplains as demand for housing increases and, when rivers flood, they are exposed to the hazard. Many rivers flood naturally in spring when snows melt. Rivers are flooding more, as shown by the floods in York.

 This response lacks confidence. There is an awareness of the increasing issue, but it is not consistently covered. The simple reference to the example comes at the end, but the theoretical points are valid. Language is less competent and the structure does not have paragraphs, a clear introduction or a conclusion. As mentioned in the introduction (p. 7), part (d) would be marked according to Levels, this one reaching Level 2, with 5 marks.

■ ■ ■

Answer to question 1: Candidate B

(a)

 Candidate B correctly identifies the differences between the hydrographs. The urban hydrograph is very steep and declines rapidly. The woodland hydrograph is lower than the pasture one. Full marks are awarded here.

(b) The urban hydrograph rises steeply and declines slightly more gently, with a very short lag time. This is because there is little vegetation to allow interception and infiltration. The urban land surface is impermeable and water runs off rapidly into the drains and reaches the river very quickly. On the other hand, the woodland hydrograph has a gentle rising limb and an even more gentle recession limb. This is because the dense vegetation intercepts most of the precipitation, causes it to reach the ground gradually and to be infiltrated. More water will reach the river as groundwater flow, with very little overland flow — hence the long lag time.

> 🖉 The command word here is important. This response does explain the differences in the shapes of the hydrographs and there is good use of appropriate geographical vocabulary and language. This is a wordy answer and some of the descriptive points might have been left out, but this is at the top of Level 2 and gains full marks.

(c) Flooding is an increasing issue in the UK, as shown by the recent flooding around York.

Flooding occurs around York for natural reasons. It is the confluence of tributaries of the River Ouse, and after a long period of rain over the Pennines the waters reach York at the same time, and the river floods. Flooding is increased if snow melt occurs or rain falls onto an already saturated surface; overland flow will be dominant.

Human influences have increased the frequency of flooding. The draining of peat on the uplands has increased water flow, and the Vale of York is arable land allowing much overland flow. Also, the increase in settlement in the Ouse basin has increased the impermeability of the land surface and water reaches the rivers more quickly via the efficient drains. More development occurs on river floodplains, meaning that more property is affected by flooding.

In conclusion, a combination of physical and human factors has increased the hazard of flooding in the UK in recent years.

> 🖉 The command word requires explanation, but the key words are *increasing* and *issue*. Simple explanations of flooding will not be totally relevant: there must be reasons for the changing occurrence. This response covers both human and physical factors applied to a case study. The factors are correctly identified, and explanation is offered. There is good use of geographical terminology and there is a clear structure to the response, with an introduction, paragraphs and a conclusion. The response covers both the *increasing* and the *issue* elements, and attains the top of Level 3, for 10 marks.

Climatic hazards and change

Study the table below which shows average precipitation (mm) for a typical station in the cool temperate western maritime (CTWM) climate.

	Jan	Feb	Mar	Apr	May	Jun	Jul	Aug	Sep	Oct	Nov	Dec	Total
Paris CTWM	60	50	35	40	60	55	60	65	55	50	50	50	**630**

(a) **Describe the annual pattern of precipitation for this climate as shown by the data for Paris.** (5 marks)

(b) **Suggest reasons for the annual pattern of precipitation in this climate.** (5 marks)

(c) **Outline the costs and benefits for human activity in areas with this climate.** (10 marks)

■ ■ ■

Answer to question 2: Candidate A

(a) In the CTWM climate, rain occurs in every month, with March the lowest (35 mm) and August the highest (65 mm).

> 𝑒 This is an accurate response, for 2 marks. There is reference to the data, though not consistently. The main patterns are identified, but reference to seasonal variations could have gained further credit.

(b) In the CTWM climate the even monthly amounts of rainfall (35–65 mm) are the result of the depressions which affect this part of the world. These occur all year. The depressions form over the Atlantic, and frontal rain falls at warm and cold fronts as they pass over this part of Europe. In summer there is more convectional rain as thunderstorms occur.

> 𝑒 This is a very generalised, yet basically correct, response, for 3 marks (at the top of Level 1). There is a clear understanding, but points are not fully developed. There are references to the data, but these are not consistently made. The response identifies the convectional rainfall in summer, but the explanation is not developed.

(c) The climate has a great influence on farming activities. In the UK, for example, the west is wetter than the east and the south is warmer than the north. This means that pastoral farming is more common in the west, whereas in the east arable predominates. Sheep are more common than cattle in the colder north, and the further south that arable farming takes place, the longer the growing season and the greater the yields. The climate also affects tourism, with more resorts on the south coast, where there is more sunshine and, in addition, warmer temperatures. This also encourages retirement to these resorts and the inland areas in the south.

Water is piped from wetter areas in the west to the drier east (e.g. from Wales to Birmingham).

e This response is unbalanced towards the benefits, and the costs are only implied. The points are valid but are generally unsupported, with reference to specific locations very minimal. Development of the disadvantages would be necessary to gain more than 5 marks out of the 10 available and reach the upper end of the Level 2 or Level 3. The extended prose style is not well developed in this case.

■ ■ ■

Answer to question 2: Candidate B

(a) Precipitation is evenly spread in the CTWM climate, occurring in all months of the year, with a range of 35 mm in March to 65 mm in August. This gives a slight summer maximum, as in the TM area, but January, the wettest winter month, does have 60 mm.

e This response does have clear elements of the pattern, so full marks are awarded. The table is used effectively to make the points, with actual data quoted.

(b) The CTWM climate is strongly influenced by the low pressure systems of the westerly wind belt. The precipitation is evenly spread as the depressions formed at the meeting of polar and tropical maritime air masses cause precipitation by frontal uplift. These are more frequent in winter when Paris would be in the track of the depressions, but they can occur all year — hence the limited monthly range from 35 to 65 mm. In summer, high-pressure systems are more frequent, but the maximum of 65 mm for August is a result of intense heating, causing convectional thunderstorms.

e This response follows the command word and provides reasons, and gains full marks. The pressure systems for summer and winter are covered and frontal precipitation identified as a major contributor. The identification of the influence of convectional precipitation in summer is the mark of a very good response at the top of Level 2. This answer would gain 5 marks.

(c) The CTWM climate provides challenges and opportunities for those living in it. Although there are few extremes in the weather, some extremes, such as intense rainfall or heavy snow and summer heatwaves, can occur. In northwest Europe, climate affects farming. The temperature and precipitation regimes show a decrease in precipitation from west to east and higher temperatures to the south. As a result, dairy and beef cattle are raised in the wetter areas in the west of the area, especially the UK, and arable crops, such as wheat, in the drier east. Northern France and northern Germany also show this pattern. The cooler temperatures in the north restrict the arable crops to other cereals, such as oats, and the livestock changes to sheep, as in upland Scotland.

Other positive effects include the stimulus to tourism in warmer and drier areas, such as the coastal areas of southern England. These areas are also favoured for retirement because of the greater amounts of sunshine and higher temperatures.

The greatest challenges come from the variability of the weather in this climatic area. The weather is rarely settled for more than a few days. Thus, a wet summer will have a great negative impact on tourism and cause losses to businesses dependent on the service sector, whereas a long hot spell in summer will result in a very good year for business, as in 1976, 1995 and 1996. However, such warm dry spells in anticyclonic conditions result in water shortages. In France in 2003 the death rate rose dramatically, especially among the elderly, because of the long period of very high temperatures (over a week above 35°C).

Therefore, the CTWM climate offers both challenges and opportunities to people.

e This is a well-argued response. The use of support comes from a number of brief references, rather than a more detailed case study, but it is consistent. Both costs and benefits are covered, and farming, tourism and general economic development are mentioned. There is a brief introduction and conclusion. This would reach the lower end of Level 3 and score 8 marks.

question 3

Energy and life

(a) Study the energy pyramid below.

Name of trophic level

Name the trophic levels in the boxes provided.	(5 marks)
(b) Why is so little energy passed on from one trophic level to the next?	(5 marks)
(c) With reference to the tropical rainforest biome, examine the factors that account for its natural productivity.	(10 marks)

■ ■ ■

Answer to question 3: Candidate A

(a) Grass, mouse, snake, bird.

> *e* This demonstrates the principles, by using examples, but does not use the correct names of the trophic levels and therefore gains no marks.

(b) The transfer of energy between trophic levels is inefficient because it is lost in the transfer. Energy is lost in breathing, living, decay and excretion. Meat eaters are inefficient users of energy in that, compared with the energy available as plants, only 1% of energy is used by the meat eaters.

> *e* This response shows some understanding of the reasons, which are offered in a rather simplistic way. Some credit can be awarded in Level 1 (3 marks). However, there is digression away from the theme into the consequences of this energy loss, which was not requested.

(c) The tropical rainforest biome is the most productive biome. The solar radiation is at its greatest all year and temperatures are high all of the time. The rainfall is high and there is no dry season, so that plants can grow all year round. This means that productivity is very great and there is much organic matter as the biomass, which is the weight of matter per metre squared. Thus there are many factors affecting productivity.

> *e* This response shows an understanding of the main concepts. Although there is no specific definition as an introduction, one is given later. There is a simple introduction and a conclusion; a number of valid factors are covered, but there is not the detailed knowledge or geographical terminology needed to gain high marks. This response reaches Level 2, for 5 marks.

■ ■ ■

Answer to question 3: Candidate B

(a) Producer, primary consumer, secondary consumer, tertiary consumer.

> *e* This is correct. Alternatively, any correct combination of plants, herbivores, carnivores, omnivores, or an acceptable alternative with a consistent classification, would gain full marks.

(b) Energy is created by solar radiation converted into organic matter by photosynthesis. At each trophic level, energy is lost by respiration, excretion, decomposition and heat; this is lost before transfer to the next level, resulting in only 10% of energy being passed on. For example, when we eat meat only 10% is converted into organic matter as the actions of breathing, excretion and living cause energy to be lost, i.e. we are unable to convert all of the material into energy.

> *e* This is a very good response. The reasons for energy loss are stated, meeting the demands of the command word, and these are exemplified. This is at the top of Level 2 and full marks are awarded. A diagram could be helpful here and would gain appropriate credit.

(c) Tropical rainforest is the most productive biome on earth.

Net primary productivity is defined as the mass (g/m^2pa) of organic matter produced after losses by respiration etc. and can be expressed thus: net primary productivity = $P - R$, where P = productivity and R = respiration.

The rainforest has ideal conditions for plant growth, with high annual temperatures (over 27°C) all year, so there is an all-year growing season. The greatest amount of solar radiation is received here, as the sun is high in the sky all year (latitude). In addition, precipitation is heavy (over 2000 mm pa) and occurs all year, and there is a water surplus available for plant growth.

Therefore, a range of factors is responsible for the productivity of this biome.

> *e* This is a very full response at the top of Level 2, for 7 marks. A range of factors is covered and examined, as required by the command word. There is a clear definition, thus setting the scene. The introduction, development of the points and the conclusion indicate a good answer. There are no specific examples quoted in this response, but the level of understanding is very good. Reference might have been made to the rate of decomposition of organic matter to maintain the nutrient cycle, so that nutrient losses are minimised. The development of these points would allow entry to Level 3.